Gardening Tools

ADVANCE PUBLISHERS

Advance Publishers, L.C.
1060 Maitland Center Commons, Suite 365
Maitland, FL 32751 USA

10 9 8 7 6 5 4 3 2 1
ISBN-10: 1-57973-390-5

One windy summer day in Sheet Rock Hills, Manny got a phone call from Abuelito.

"¡Hola, Manny!" Abuelito said. "I'm at the community garden, and the wind has blown over some of the *plantas*. They could really use your help!"

"Poor little plants," Manny said. "We'll be right over!"

The weather affects everyone and everything!

WEATHER
Weather is made up of different things, such as wind, temperature, sunshine, and clouds.

As Manny and the tools stepped outside, Mr. Lopart went sailing right by them on his office chair! The wind was blowing him down the street. "Mr. Lopart," Manny called after him. "Can we help you?"

WEATHER

The windiest place on the earth is Port Martin, Antarctica. For a month, it has winds blowing as fast as 65 miles an hour. That's as fast as a speeding car!

"No thank you," Mr Lopart called back, his voice trailing off in the wind. "I have everything under controlll."

WIND

You can't see the wind. But you can feel it. It can feel very strong and powerful. It can also be a soft, gentle breeze.

Mrs. Portillo was outside hanging laundry to dry in the wind.

"There's nothing like a hard-blowing *viento* to dry things fast," she said.

When Manny told her where they were headed, Mrs. Portillo asked Manny if they could bring her back some vegetables from the community garden.

Nature makes the wind work for it, too.

WIND

The wind carries little seeds from one place to another. Wherever the seeds land, they have a chance to grow into new plants. So, the flowers in your backyard may have been blown there from miles away.

The Community Garden has lots of different kinds of plants.

GARDENS

A garden is a place where people grow plants. A garden can have vegetables, fruits, or flowers ... or all of these plants growing together.

At the garden, Abuelito was busy replanting tomato plants that had blown over in the wind.

"They're still small because the weather has been so cold," Abuelito explained. "They need special care right now. These little *plantas* are not strong enough yet to stand up to such a big wind."

The little tomato plants need more sunshine to grow big and strong.

GARDENS
Every garden needs some very special things in order to grow. These tomatoes, for instance, need lots of sunshine. Their long stems, called vines, grow up toward the sun.

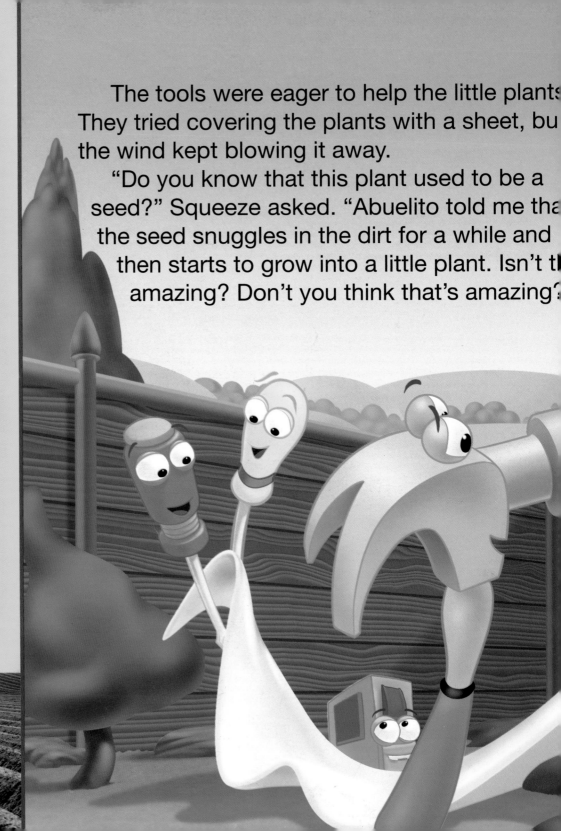

Squeeze thinks soil is stupendous!

SOIL

Plants need soil to help them stand up tall and strong, and to keep their roots safe. Soil also has nutrients and water that help plants grow.

The tools were eager to help the little plants. They tried covering the plants with a sheet, but the wind kept blowing it away.

"Do you know that this plant used to be a seed?" Squeeze asked. "Abuelito told me that the seed snuggles in the dirt for a while and then starts to grow into a little plant. Isn't that amazing? Don't you think that's amazing?"

SEEDLINGS

After getting
plenty of water and
warmth, a little stem
starts to poke out of
the top of the seed,
pushing its way up
and out of the soil.
Soon the stem may
grow leaves and
become a big plant!

Sunflowers grow to be much bigger than Rusty.

"Maybe if we put clothes on the toma[...] and other plants, they'll be warmer and g[...] faster," Dusty suggested.

"I don't think we have clothes that will f[...] all of the plants in the garden," Rusty said.

SUNFLOWERS

Sunflowers are the tallest flowers in the world. Some have grown to be more than 25 feet high. That's taller than a giraffe!

The sunflowers are so tall, and the strawberries are so short…"

"We'd better ask Manny what to do," Pat said.

HAIL

Hailstones are lumps or balls of ice that fall from the sky. They are formed when raindrops pass through an area of cold air on their way to the earth.

Manny said that what the plants really needed were some strong wooden trellises and supports to lean on. Manny and the tools went to the hardware store to get supplies.

"Did you hear," Kelly asked them, "that we might get a hailstorm later today?"

"That would be very bad for the plants," Manny said. "We'd better hurry! *¡Muy rapido!*"

HAILSTONES

Hailstones range in size, with most falling between the size of gum balls and golf balls. The largest hailstone ever recorded was the size of a large grapefruit. It was nearly 7 inches long and weighed almost 2 pounds!

FRUIT

A fruit is a part of a plant we can eat that contains seeds. Some fruits have several seeds, while others have one large seed that can be found inside their pit.

Manny and the tools got right to work building sturdy supports for the plants at the community garden.

"This will protect the fruits and vegetables so they grow up to be ripe and delicious," Manny said.

Turner probably likes sour lemons too!

FRUIT

Fruits can be soft and sweet like bananas, tart and crispy like apples, or even sour and juicy like lemons.

"I think peaches are the most *delicioso* fruit," Felipe said.

"I like watermelon best," Stretch said.

"Well, I like sour cherries," Turner said in his most sour voice, and everyone—even Turner—laughed.

VEGETABLES

Vegetables are the
parts of plants that
we can eat! Lettuce
is one plant's leaves;
celery is another's
stem; broccoli is
a flower; and
beets are roots.
Vegetables are
healthy foods that
are full of vitamins
and nutrients.

When their work was done at the communi
garden, Abuelito asked Manny and the tools to
come to his greenhouse.

"I told Mrs. Portillo that I would send her
some vegetables from the community garden.
Those verduras aren't ripe yet, but mine have
been safe and warm here in the greenhouse.
They're ripe and ready to pick," Abuelito said.

Abuelito's greenhouse is a good place to grow vegetables.

VEGETABLES

Farmers grow a lot of vegetables. Other people grow vegetables right in their own backyards. You can even grow some vegetables on your windowsill!

Abuelito is happy to share his colorful harvest with Mrs. Portillo.

TOMATOES

The tomato is really a fruit! Scientifically speaking, it has all the characteristics of a fruit. But because the tomato is often used as a vegetable and is not sweet like most fruits, many people consider the tomato a vegetable.

Manny and the tools helped Abuelito pick armloads of vegetables from his greenhouse. Bright red tomatoes and dark green peppers. Sweet white onions and strong-smelling cilantro.

Then they brought the vegetables into town for rs. Portillo.

When Manny eats cilantro, he's eating leaves!

LEAVES

If you have ever eaten lettuce or spinach, then you've tasted plant leaves! You've probably also tasted herb leaves, such as mint, rosemary, basil, and oregano, which add flavor to many of the foods we eat.

RAIN
Rain forms when the water vapor that forms clouds turns into droplets of water and falls from the sky.

"This is just what I need to make my salsa!" Mrs. Portillo said.

"Then why are you crying?" Turner asked suspiciously.

"Onions always make me cry," Mrs. Portillo said, "but I'm really *¡muy feliz*—very happy!"

"I'm happy, too," Manny said, "because it's warm and raining outside instead of cold and hailing. And that's good news for the community garden!"

The rain will help the plants at the community

RAIN

Rain soaks into the ground, giving trees, grass, flowers, fruits, and vegetables the water they need to grow.

Back at the shop, Manny called Abuelito. "Mrs. Portillo wants to thank you in person for the vegetables you sent from your garden, Abuelito. We're all invited to her house for dinner tonight!," Manny said. "And guess what's on the menu—Mrs. Portillo's famous fresh salsa!"